To the reader:

Welcome to the DK ELT Graded Readers! These readers are different. They explore aspects of the world around us: its history, geography, science … and a lot of other things. And they show the different ways in which people live now, and lived in the past.

These DK ELT Graded Readers give you material for reading for information, and reading for pleasure. You are using your English to do something real. The illustrations will help you understand the text, and also help bring the Reader to life. There is a glossary to help you understand the special words for this topic. Listen to the cassette or CD as well, and you can really enter the world of the Olympic Games, the *Titanic*, or the Trojan War … and a lot more. Choose the topics that interest you, improve your English, and learn something … all at the same time.
Enjoy the series!

To the teacher:

This series provides varied reading practice at five levels of language difficulty, from elementary to FCE level:
BEGINNER
ELEMENTARY A
ELEMENTARY B
INTERMEDIATE
UPPER INTERMEDIATE
The language syllabus has been designed to suit the factual nature of the series, and includes a wider vocabulary range than is usual with ELT readers: language linked with the specific theme of each book is included and glossed. The language scheme, and ideas for exploiting the material (including the recorded material) both in and out of class are contained in the Teacher's Resource Book.
We hope you and your students enjoy using this series.

A DORLING KINDERSLEY BOOK

DK www.dk.com

Originally published as Eyewitness Reader
Days of the Knights in 1998 and adapted as
an ELT Graded Reader for
Dorling Kindersley by

studio cactus ©

13 SOUTHGATE STREET WINCHESTER HAMPSHIRE SO23 9DZ

Published in Great Britain by
Dorling Kindersley Limited
9 Henrietta Street, London WC2E 8PS

2 4 6 8 10 9 7 5 3 1

Copyright © 2000
Dorling Kindersley Limited, London

All rights reserved. No part of this publication
may be reproduced, stored in a retrieval system,
or transmitted in any form or by any means,
electronic, mechanical, photocopying, recording, or
otherwise, without the prior written permission of
the copyright owner.

A CIP catalogue record for this book is
available from the British Library.

ISBN 0-7513-3198-8

Colour reproduction by Colourscan, Singapore
Printed and bound in China
by L. Rex Printing Co., Ltd
Text film output by Ocean Colour, UK

The publisher would like to thank the following for
their kind permission to reproduce their photographs:
c=centre; t=top; b=below; l=left; r=right

Ancient, Art and Architecture: Ronald Sheridan 5cr; 10tl, 27br;
AKG, London: 29cr; **Board of Trustees of the Armouries:** 21br;
Bridgeman Art Library, London: Biblioteca Estense, Modena 16tl;
Bibliotheque de L'Arsenal, Paris 37l; British Library 6tl, 10cl, 14bl,
27tr, 35tr; Bibliotheque Nationale, Paris 3c, 6cl, 9tr; Ecole des Beaux
Arts, Paris, Giraudon 30cl; Fitzwilliam Museum, University of
Cambridge 26bc; Musee Conde, Chantilly, France, Giraudon 36b;
Victoria & Albert Museum, London 32tl; **British Museum, London:**
39tr; **English Heritage:** 32bl, 38br, 46bl; Ivan Lapper 46tl;
ETArchive: 29tr, 38tl; Bibliotheque Nationale, Paris 5tr, 9br;
Mary Evans Picture Library: 14tl,16cl, 23cr, 38cl; Explorer 24bl;
Institution of Civil Engineers 1br, 20tr, 47cl; **Robert Harding
Picture Library:** British Library 24tl, 40b; **The Marsden Archive:**
Simon Marsden 45tr; **Museum of London:** 39cr, 43cr;
Wallace Collection: 20l, 21cl, 47tr

Jacket credit: **Wallace Collection:** background

Additional photography by Geoff Brightling, Geoff Dann,
Mike Dunning, Dave King, Tim Ridley, and Jerry Young.

Contents

DK ELT Graded Readers

UPPER INTERMEDIATE

KNIGHTS AND CASTLES

Written by
David Maule

Series Editor Susan Holden

DK

London • New York • Delhi • Sydney

Under Attack!

It was early morning and the light was growing. The sentries in the towers rubbed their eyes and thought of breakfast.

"Did you hear something?" one of the men above the main gate said. The others listened.

"Wagons." They could all hear the creak of the wheels now – lots of wagons. But it wasn't market day, and it was too early in the morning.

"Look!" another said. There were dark shapes moving in the mist. Men – hundreds of them.

"Sound the alarm!" an officer shouted. "Quick! We're under attack!"

Enemy soldiers had reached the castle before the guards knew what was happening.

They were taking the place by surprise, just as the Baron had planned. For years, the Baron and Sir Henry, the lord of the castle, had been enemies. Lately, Lord Henry had decided to make his castle stronger. The Baron knew it would be more difficult to capture if he waited. He decided the time had come to attack.

The soldiers in the castle knew what to do. The gate was always shut at night, but now they made sure that the heaviest bars were in place. Then, they went to the big wheels and pulled up the drawbridge.

At the same time, others rushed to the battlements – the tops of the castle walls – which had spaces between the stones for them to shoot through. Each man carried either a longbow or a crossbow. The longbows could shoot an arrow three hundred metres. At a closer distance, they could drive it through 1cm of steel, and a good bowman could send off 15 arrows in a minute.

The crossbows were more powerful, but they were much slower, and not very accurate. As well as the bows, there were piles of stones along the walls ready to be dropped on anybody who tried to climb up.

Down below, the Baron's soldiers shouted insults at the men on the battlements. They had surrounded the castle. There was no escape!

Battlements
These gave soldiers some protection while shooting through the gaps, called crenels.

Drawbridge
This was lifted to cover the entrance. Inside was the portcullis, made of crossed pieces of wood. This was lowered during attacks.

Garrison
These were the soldiers who defended a castle. They were either knights or hired men.

Siege camp
The enemy set up a siege camp to eat and sleep in. It was near the castle but far enough away to be safe from arrows.

There was a village not far away. The people there normally felt safe. They paid their taxes to Lord Henry and expected his soldiers to protect them. In times of danger, they could go to the castle.

But today there was no warning. The first the villagers knew of the attack was when soldiers rushed down the muddy street and started to knock down their doors. Some of the people jumped through windows and tried to run away. A few succeeded, because the soldiers had not bothered to surround the whole village. But most were hunted down and killed near their houses. Others tried to stay inside. The soldiers either broke the doors down or set fire to the roofs and waited till they ran out screaming. Many died that day – men, women, and children.

The soldiers stole everything. They took beds, chairs, and food. They took pigs, chickens, ducks, anything that could be turned into a meal. Then they set fire to the rest of the houses and left.

The soldiers in the castle saw the fires and heard the cries and screams of the villagers. Many of them had friends or family there, but there was nothing they could do. If they left the castle to try to help, they would simply die.

Now a train of wagons, pulled by cattle, moved slowly up to the castle. As the smoke from the village filled the air, the Baron's soldiers began to unpack tents, food, and weapons. They were setting up a siege camp. They were going to surround the castle and attack either until they broke in or the soldiers inside ran out of food. They needed somewhere to live while the days, weeks, and maybe months passed.

Catapult
Besides throwing rocks, large catapults were used to send dead animals over the castle walls. This spread disease among the people inside.

It was late afternoon before everything was in place. Armed men were all around the castle. Large catapults, which could throw rocks a great distance, stood ready. The Baron even had a few new cannons, though these were quite small.

Two men left the Baron's camp and walked towards the castle. When they were near the main gate, one of them raised a trumpet and blew a long note. The other man shouted, "The Baron says surrender now or die later."

Lord Henry was standing on the walls above. "Never," he shouted back.

The two men turned and walked back to the camp, and the attack began. Rocks from the catapults flew towards the castle walls. The cannons crashed and smoke blew across the ground. Bowmen moved forward and shot burning arrows into the castle, and soon smoke could be seen rising from inside. Some of the Baron's soldiers ran forward and dropped large pieces of wood and sacks of earth into the moat – the water-filled ditch around the castle – to make a bridge to the walls.

In the Baron's camp, many of his men were busy making a siege tower. It had three floors inside, each connected by a ladder. At the top, it was as high as the castle walls. The outside was covered with wood to protect the soldiers inside.

At the same time, other men put together a battering ram. This was a long, thick piece of wood, made from a whole tree, and placed on a set of wooden wheels so that it could be pulled forward. At the front, was a large piece of metal in the shape of the head of a ram – a male sheep. All of this was covered with a wooden roof to protect the soldiers.

Soon everything was ready. Before the main gate and in front of the lowest part of the wall, the moat had been filled in. Pieces of wood had been laid on top. Many men had died putting these in place, but now there were two roads to the castle walls.

The siege tower began to move forward. The defenders shot arrows at it, but these had little effect. Sometimes an arrow would find a hole in the tower, and a cry was heard from inside, but the tower kept coming. When it was a few metres from the walls, Lord Henry's men pushed out long pieces of wood to hold it back. But there were more people pushing from below, and still it came on.

Bows
An English longbow of the time had a pulling power of about 45kg.

Siege tower
When this tower was pushed up to the castle wall, the attacking soldiers could climb into the castle.

Bombard
This gun fired large stone balls that could break down the walls of a castle.

Hostages
Soldiers took important prisoners to their castle. The prisoners were set free when money was paid in exchange for them.

When the tower was only a couple of metres away, some of Lord Henry's most experienced men rushed forward and jumped the gap. There was a fierce fight on the top platform. This allowed other defenders to tie ropes to the tower, and start to pull it over. At the main gate, the men on the ram were hammering at the drawbridge, without much success. When they realized they were alone, they left the ram and ran away. The attack had failed.

The Baron waited in his camp. After a few weeks, the defenders started to run short of food. There was no fresh meat. Most days the soldiers only had a small piece of bread to eat. Then, one day, they looked out and saw something that meant the end. The Baron had got a huge cannon, called a bombard. His men were dragging it into position. The defenders' hearts sank.

Late that night, a group of men left the castle in secret. They begged the enemy soldiers to take them to the Baron.

"Get my men into the castle, and I will allow you to live," he said.

The men led a small number of enemy knights to a secret entrance. The Baron's men slipped into the castle, killed the men who were on watch, and opened the gates. The Baron's army rushed in and soon the great castle was taken.

The soldiers ran through every part of the castle, from the tops of the walls to the prisons down below ground level. They killed Lord Henry and his wife, and carried their bodies to the Baron. The rest of the family could be taken as hostages, but the Baron had said that Lord Henry and his wife were to die. He wanted no chance of the family coming back to attack him later.

However, there was one they overlooked. Lord Henry's son Thomas, little more than a baby, was carried by his nursemaid through a secret door and out of the castle.

Looting
Gold, silver, jewellery, and clothing were carried off by looters. They also took away money that the lord had collected from taxes.

Fairs
Small fairs lasted
a few days. Bigger
ones might run for
a week.

Merchants
These men
travelled to places
far away and
brought back fine
things to sell, such
as cloth, glassware,
and unusual spices.

Fairs and Holy Days

"Look there!" Thomas pulled on his nurse's skirt. "That man's standing on his hands!"

Mary looked down at him and smiled. She thought back to the terrible time when she had run through the Baron's soldiers with him in her arms. Fortunately, most of them were too busy stealing things to notice her run to the forest.

There, she got help from men who had followed Sir Henry. They took her and the boy to his uncle's house. Thomas grew up there. He was seven now, and a fine strong boy. Today he was excited. The nearby village was having a fair for the feast of St Dunstan. There was a lot to see.

The best jugglers spent years learning to do it well. Some could juggle seven balls at once!

As well as merchants from distant places, there were some selling the more everyday things that the people needed. Here was a man who had walked from the sea with a basket of fish on his back. Women stood around with eggs, meat, fruit and vegetables, and honey. Thomas' nurse was hoping a merchant would turn up with some fine cloth. There! She could see some. She moved closer and began to talk about prices.

Thomas didn't care about cloth. He was watching a man with a dancing bear. Then his eye was caught by a juggler. He couldn't remember seeing anything as clever before.

Mummers
These travelling actors often performed religious plays.

Wine and ale
Most people drank ale, which was like beer. Wine was very expensive.

It was afternoon before Thomas and his nurse got back to his uncle's castle. He found the place alive with excitement. Everybody wanted to join in the fun. Nobody would do any work today.

The reason for it all was that a group of travelling actors, called mummers, had arrived the night before. Today, in the castle courtyard, they were going to put on a play called *Noah and the Great Flood*. The story would be complete with costumes, songs, and sound effects. The chance of entertainment didn't come very often, and all of this was a good excuse for a holiday.

Everybody who lived in the castle was now in the courtyard, and many others as well. Some of the performers from the market had come to entertain the crowd – the jugglers and the singers, even the man with the dancing bear. There were food sellers as well, with nuts and fruit and cakes. They knew they could make money while the crowd waited.

There were free things too, because Thomas' uncle was a generous man. A pig and a cow had been killed, and were now roasting over a fire. The baker had been told to make a lot of bread and give it away. And there was wine for the knights and their ladies, and ale for the rest.

Now a group of children moved through the crowd that had gathered to watch.

Pouring wine at festival time.

"Let me through!" shouted Thomas. "I can't see anything!"

They made some space for him at the front. The mummers had built a raised platform in the middle of the courtyard. One of them now climbed the steps and began to speak.

"I am Noah," he said, putting one hand to his long false beard.

For the next hour or so, Thomas was completely lost in wonder as the play went on. Of course, he knew the story, but this really brought it to life. At the end, he clapped and cheered with all the others.

More entertainment followed. A group of acrobats took over the stage. Travelling musicians, called minstrels, sang to the crowd. Later, in the evening, in the great hall, those same minstrels sang for Thomas' uncle and his guests. They sang songs and told stories of faraway battles and famous heroes. Thomas, tired as he was, liked this more than any other part of this interesting day.

Minstrels
Travelling musicians entertained people, and brought news and gossip from other places.

A minstrel playing a hornpipe.

Page
A page was taught polite manners and how to use weapons.

Squire
His main job was to look after a knight's armour and weapons.

Dubbing
After he was touched on the shoulders with a sword, a squire became a knight.

Knight School

"Attack, men!" Thomas yelled. At his signal, the young soldiers rushed across the courtyard and into the great hall. But no one took any notice. Thomas and his soldiers were only six years old!

But when Thomas was seven, everything changed. He left his uncle's castle to live in another, much larger castle. There he became a page. There were quite a few pages in the castle, and, at first, Thomas was one of the smallest. He had to do what everybody told him.

He learned to ride, and how to use a sword and shield and the lance that knights carried on horseback. He spent long hours in the schoolroom learning to read and write. He was lucky in this way. In most castles, it was thought that reading and writing were only for priests.

When he was 14, Thomas became a squire. This meant that he worked for a knight. He had to keep the knight's armour and weapons clean and make sure his clothes were washed – or wash them himself, if there was nobody else to do it. He had to brush and feed the horses every day, and to help his knight at all times.

It was hard work, but Thomas enjoyed it. On one occasion, Thomas had to follow his master into battle. He was close enough to the fighting to feel afraid, and wondered how he would perform when he became a knight.

This happened when he was 20. He had now proved himself. Once, when the king visited, there was a ceremony. It became mixed up in his mind, but he remembered the words: "Rise, Sir Thomas."

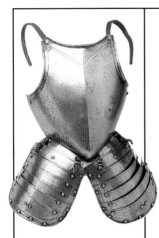

Putting on armour
Each piece of armour was tied in place with long leather straps.

Dressed to Kill

"Sir Thomas, please stand still," said his squire. H placed his foot on the knight's back, and pulled o the leather straps.

"Sorry, Roger," Thomas said. Usually he helped more to put on the armour, but today his thoughts were somewhere else. It was still rather strange to him. He was a knight, but he had not been one for very long. He realized that he knew Roger's job much better than he knew his own. Well, he would have to learn fast, because this wa the day of the tournament. Very soon, he would have to act like a knight rather than a squire.

"Roger, do you think Lady Elaine will be watching?" Thomas asked.

The squire rolled his eyes. "Probably, Sir," he answered. "But if you don't hurry, Sir, you may miss the tournament – and Lady Elaine."

Thomas smiled. He would be so disappointed if Lady Elaine wasn't there, but there was no reason why she shouldn't be. Everybody who lived in the castle was coming to the tournament, and many more besides. There would be knights there from all parts of the country – even some from other lands. Most of them would have a lady watching them, and the lucky ones would carry her handkerchief on their lance.

Thomas didn't think he could ask for Lady Elaine's handkerchief. There wasn't very much between them – just a look and one or two smiles. They had hardly even spoken to each other. Perhaps if he won, he would ask her next time.

He grunted as Roger pulled hard on one of the breastplate straps. He had already strapped four pieces of armour to each of Thomas' legs. Thomas held up a hand. "Just a moment, Roger. I've got an itch."

Roger looked like he wanted to hit his master. Instead he scratched the itch and went back to his work. Then Roger handed Thomas his gauntlets and stepped back. He looked Thomas up and down. "You'll do," he said. "Try not to get it dirty."

Thomas smiled.

Helmet

Breastplate

Gauntlet (metal glove)

Spur

Armour
A well-made suit of armour was expensive. It was like buying a new car today.

The suit of armour was made from the finest German steel. But it had been in the family for many years. It looked a little old-fashioned, and it was dented all over. Thomas didn't have the money to pay an armour-maker to hammer out the dents. When he first got it, Roger had spent a long time working with sand and water to get the rust off the metal. He had done well, and now at least it shined, but it would never look very good again, and Thomas felt a little ashamed.

Even worse than the well-worn armour was the condition of Thomas' weapons. His shield was just as dented as the armour, and had long, deep scratches running across it. His lance, the long spear that knights used on horseback, was brightly painted, but in some places the paint had started to fall off.

That probably meant it had been used, but perhaps not too many times, because tournament lances were designed to break. That was why knights usually had a few spare ones standing in the ground outside their tents. If Thomas broke his only lance, he would have to borrow one from somebody else, and pay for it later if he broke it. His only good weapon was his sword. It had belonged to his father and was found after the attack.

His uncle had kept it until Thomas was knighted. It had a fine silver handle, though this also had a few dents and scratches. The blade had been made in Germany, with the handle put on later in England. When he had some money, a silversmith could make that handle look like new again, but there was no need to do anything to the blade except keep it polished and razor-sharp.

When he had money ... That was the problem. Family connections had given Thomas the chance to become a knight, but he was a knight without land or property. Today might be his first chance to do something about it. If he could knock another knight off his horse, he would win both the horse and the man's armour. He might even sell them back to the knight who had owned them. The loser was usually ready to pay a good price, since it saved all the trouble of training a new horse and getting fitted with a new suit of armour.

"The first money I get will go towards a new set of weapons," Thomas told Roger. "I'll buy a good, heavy mace and have my sword handle repaired. And I'll get at least three spare lances, though you won't like having to carry them."

A tournament was only one way to earn money. Battles could also be profitable. Thomas promised himself he would try to get into a battle, and make sure he got a good share of what was stolen afterwards.

Mace
The heavy metal end of this could break bones through armour. Maces were used mainly when fighting on foot.

21

When Thomas was ready, he walked to the tournament field. He was beginning to feel more comfortable in his armour, which had been as unfamiliar as any new suit of clothes when he first put it on. He noticed Lady Elaine standing at the edge of the jousting area. This immediately took his mind off his worries, and he went and stood beside her. They had very little to say to each other at first, but Thomas was able to tell her the names of the knights rushing towards each other on their horses.

Horse armour
Horses were dressed in full armour for battle, but for a tournament only their heads were protected. This metal face armour was called a shaffron.

Jousts
One popular tournament event was the joust. Knights on horseback rushed at each other with long lances.

22

Two knights competing in a joust.

The faces of the knights were hidden by helmets, but Thomas knew each one by his colours.

Over his armour, a knight wore a sleeveless coat sewn with the badge that belonged to his family. The knight's horses also wore cloths in the family colours. Thomas had studied these as part of his training. In the library at the castle were great books with coloured drawings, showing not only the English families but also those of other countries. Thomas had spent days and weeks memorizing them.

Helmets
Jousting helmets were three times heavier than war helmets.

Coat of arms
The badge and colours of a family were known as its coat of arms. This was passed down from a father to his eldest son.

23

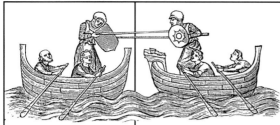

Water jousts
Sometimes knights jousted from boats. Jousting lances were made from hollow wood that would break and do less harm than solid lances.

How to win
If you knocked a knight out of his saddle, you would win. You also got points for breaking your lance on his shield.

Tournaments were great occasions, and people came from far away to join in the fun. But for the knights, who provided the main interest, things were more serious. Jousting was a way of practising the skills they would use in battle.

Death was possible, broken bones more likely and recovery was a slow and painful business. Only the most experienced knights could lower their lance, look across the field at their opponent, and not feel nervous.

Thomas felt more than nervous. His mouth was dry and his hands felt cold and wet. When his turn came, he kicked his horse forward like a man in a dream. Far away across the field, he saw his opponent. His coat and shield showed a black eagle with two heads.

Thomas focused his eyes on the eagle on the shield. The centre of its back would be a good spot. If he could hit that with his lance, he should knock the knight to the ground.

The signal came, and Thomas got his horse moving. He moved the point of his lance down, realizing that he should have done this earlier. He had just enough time to get it lined up when the two of them met.

He felt a violent blow on his left arm, swung in the saddle but managed to stay on his horse. He was looking at the broken end of his lance. That would be worth some points. Then his head cleared and he heard the cheering of the crowd. He looked round. The man wearing the two-headed eagle was just getting up from the ground.

Thomas smiled, and shook his head. He couldn't really believe that he'd done it. He looked at the man's horse, which had slowed to a walk. It was his now, as was the armour. His eyes looked over the crowd. Lady Elaine was standing where she had been before. Her eyes were shining, and she was smiling at him.

Estate
All of a lord's lands, even when they were spread far across the country, were part of his estate.

Build it Strong

Thomas unrolled the document and studied it carefully. It took him some time to understand it.

"Well, well," he said at last. "The king has decided to give me permission to build a castle."

He looked up and smiled at his wife. "We're going to be busy," he said.

Royal writ
A king gave orders through documents known as writs. These might give land, or the right to hunt, or demand taxes.

The royal seal made the document official.

An artist decorated the writ with plants, birds, animals, and patterns when words did not fill up all the space.

"It's taken him long enough to make up his mind," Lady Elaine said. "After all, you fought for him for years. How many battles was it?"

"Er ... five," Thomas said, "if you don't count the little ones."

He thought of the little ones. Some of them had been quite dangerous as well. "But I didn't do so badly out of it," he added. "He made me a lord, gave me land, and the wars made me rich."

"Yes, I know," Lady Elaine said. "But permission to build a castle means that he trusts you. I'm glad he's finally decided that he does."

"Yes, dear," Thomas said. There was no point in arguing with her. Lady Elaine didn't like the king, and never had.

Thomas looked at the writ again. It meant that, for at least the next ten years, he would be busy – that was if he had enough money to finish the job. Still, it had to be done. He had been born in a castle, and the Baron had burned it down. There was no need to take revenge. The Baron had chosen the wrong side, and in the end he had died for it. But Thomas felt that he owed it to his father to build another castle.

The first thing was to find a master mason, who would design the castle and watch over the building of it. Master James might be the best for the job. He had a good reputation and had done a lot of work in the area.

He thought of the best location. Most of his land was quite flat, but there was one place where the river curved around some higher ground. That might do, but Master James would have to see it first.

Lord
A lord also acted as local judge. He made decisions on disagreements among the people living on his land.

Master mason
Master masons travelled the country, working on several castles at a time.

Sleep well

Only rich people had proper beds. The very rich had feather mattresses, but most mattresses were filled with straw.

The castle had to be strong. Thomas couldn't remember anything of the attack on his father's castle, but his nursemaid had told him all about it It was a bombard that had won it for the Baron, and in the years since, bombards had become bigger and better. But castle design had changed as well. There were more outer walls and ditches now, to keep the guns away from the walls. Maste James would know all the latest methods.

Canopy

Warm, woollen curtains

Woven-straw mattress

Wheel-out bed for children or servants

Other things were important too, besides defence. The castle would also have to be beautiful inside, fine enough to impress important guests. Travel was difficult and dangerous, and visitors often stayed for weeks. They would need comfortable rooms where they could relax.

There would have to be a great hall for entertaining, of course. Thomas thought for a moment about how it might look inside, but he did not have many ideas. Perhaps Lady Elaine and Master James could decide that between them. As long as it was impressive he didn't mind. He wanted to hold a lot of concerts and feasts. He only hoped there would be enough money left over to pay for them.

Above all, the castle had to be a comfortable home for his family, his knights, and his servants. There would be private rooms for his wife and children, a full wine cellar, and a huge kitchen.

Of course, there would be a chapel where the priest could say mass and bless Thomas' family. These days, Thomas felt he had a lot to be thankful for.

He thought back over the years. It had all started very badly, with the attack on his father's castle. He had been lucky to escape with his life, and he had never known his father or mother. Now he had a wife and children of his own, and their lives were very different. But the fear of attack was deep inside him. The danger was still there. That was why he had made himself strong, and would make himself stronger.

Knight
Knights helped their lords keep control over their lands.

Chapel
A lord would have a small family chapel near his rooms and a bigger one in the courtyard for his servants.

29

Moat
A moat was a good defence during an attack. It was also a great place to fish!

Artisans
Skilled workers such as carpenters and stonemasons spent many years learning their trades. Stonemasons were the most highly paid of all artisans.

A few days later, Lord Thomas and Master James stood on the site of the castle. Each of them was an expert in his own way. Master James knew a lot about building castles; Lord Thomas, from his experience in the wars, knew something about knocking them down.

"You should be fairly safe from guns on this side," Master James said. He swept his arm round, taking in the bend in the river. "The ground over there is marshy, and even if they got the guns in, and made a hole in the wall, they would still have to swim the river."

Thomas nodded. "It's the open side that worries me. What can you do?"

He turned to look at the ground that ran downhill from where they were standing.

"Walls, and more walls," Master James said. "That's the modern way. You can't rely on one wall any more, even if it is ten feet thick. You have to keep the guns far away. So, lots of walls, and great big ditches in between them. You defend each of them until they're taken, and hope that help comes before they get close enough."

"Fine," said Thomas, "But I want a moat, too."

Master James blew out some air between his lips. "We'll have to dig deep over there where the ground rises."

"So, dig," said Thomas.

"It's your money," said Master James.

"I know," Thomas said. He thought of what Master James had said earlier, that castles were going out of date. He was right, of course. Guns would be the end of them, even as one day they would be the end of knights in armour.

Once Lord Thomas had approved the plans, things started to move quickly. Carts appeared at the site every day, bringing in stone, wood, and all the other materials needed. Workers were hired from the nearby villages. They would do the moving and the carrying, but stonemasons and carpenters came from further away, called in by Master James.

Chisels to cut stone

Hammer to hit chisels

Plumb-line to check that vertical lines are straight

Dividers to measure exact distances

Trowel to mix mortar from sand and lime

Gatehouse
Sometimes rich prisoners were kept in the gatehouse. Poor ones died in dungeons.

Murder holes
These were holes in the roof behind the portcullis. Bowmen would fire arrows at attackers through these small gaps.

On Guard!

While the castle was being built, Lord Thomas made a few changes. He worried constantly about an attack. With so many people living within the walls, he would not sleep well unless he knew the castle was as strong as possible.

One day, he called Master James into his study and they went over the plans together. "I'm not happy with the gatehouse," he said.

"What's wrong with it?" the master mason said. He was a blunt speaker. Because he was such an expert in his field, he could afford to be. He gave his clients respect, but always made it clear who knew most about building castles. Lord Thomas didn't mind this. He knew what he wanted, and he could be just as blunt.

"I don't think it's strong enough," Lord Thomas said.

"It's the right size of gatehouse for this size of castle." Master James sounded slightly offended.

Lord Thomas shook his head. "I want it bigger," he said, "with a proper tower on top, two stories high above the walls. I want somewhere safe for my family if everything else fails."

Master James looked at his client. Of course, he knew the story of the attack on his father's castle. Obviously, it still worried Lord Thomas. "It'll cost you extra. And if things get that bad, it won't protect you for long," he said.

"Build it," Lord Thomas said.

Inside the gateway, Master James placed a gate made of crossed pieces of oak and iron. This was called a portcullis.

Crime
Thieves were
punished harshly.
They risked
having a hand
cut off.

Pedlars
These traders were
usually poor. They
made a little
money selling
things such as
pots, knives, and
brushes.

The extra work on the bigger gatehouse and
tower made the job longer, and it was twelve
years before the castle was complete. But in the
end, Lord Thomas and his family had a home
that they could be proud of. Of course, they
shared it with many people. In the courtyard,
against the castle walls, were workshops for
tailors, potters, carpenters, and many others.
Peasants came to buy the things they needed.
Pedlars came to sell small things such as
buttons and ribbons.

Lord Thomas wanted the castle to be a safe place to do business. Any suspicious-looking stranger was liable to be questioned, and might well be turned away. Sometimes a man would try to bribe a guard, but this never worked. Lord Thomas paid them well and was a good lord to work for.

The castle was the centre of Lord Thomas' estate. Peasants came there to pay their taxes, and in the castle, Lord Thomas held his court. This could decide over disagreements between people, but it also had the power to try people for crimes, and to punish the guilty. When he sat in the court, Lord Thomas sat under a painting of the king's crown. This meant that he decided things in the name of the king.

If necessary, he could order a guilty person to be hanged. This did not happen very often, because Lord Thomas ran his estates well, but he could be a hard man when it was necessary. People knew they could expect a fair trial at the castle. The same was not true on many estates, where the lord used his power to make money for himself.

Peasants
Some peasants were free, but others were like slaves to the lord. They worked on his land and could not leave it.

Royal visit
It took weeks
to prepare for a
visit from a king.
Almost 100 people
would come
to stay!

The Visitor

Lord Thomas was discussing the finances of the estate with his steward, and he hardly heard the horse arriving at speed in the courtyard outside. A few minutes later a servant came in with a letter. Thomas opened it, noticed the royal seal, and read it hurriedly.

"You say that the estate is in profit?" he said to his steward.

"Yes, my lord."

"That's good, Michael. We'll need the money. The king is coming to stay."

A king and his nobles riding towards a castle.

He left the room in a hurry. "Where is Lady Elaine?" he asked the guard standing by the door.

"I heard she was in the kitchen, my lord." That was possible. Usually on a Friday she would discuss the following week's menus with the head cook. Most ladies would have called the cook upstairs, but it was typical of Elaine to go and see him. Of course, it also gave her a good excuse to look around the kitchen and make sure that everything was as it should be.

"Find her," Lord Thomas said. "Tell her ... ask her to meet me here."

"Yes, my lord."

The guard left quickly. The servant who had brought the message was still there.

"My lord – the messenger will want a reply."

Lord Thomas clapped a hand to his head. "Reply! Of course." He went back into his room, where there was paper and ink, and wrote out an answer. Of course, it was "yes". Nobody refused a visit from the king. Quickly, he attached his seal and handed the letter to the servant. "Give that to him," he said. "Give him food, drink ... anything he wants. And send for my tailor."

Lady Elaine arrived and he told her the news. When the tailor came, they discussed the new outfits they would need. Thomas wanted a short robe with fur on the ends of the sleeves. He also ordered the latest style of hat. Lady Elaine was looking for an excuse to order a new dress.

Next, Thomas turned his thoughts to entertainment. During the day there would be hunting and hawking for his guests, and at night they would enjoy music and feasts.

Clothing
There were no clothes shops like today. Everything was made by hand. Only the rich could afford good clothes.

Shoes
Wooden platforms, called pattens, were worn under shoes to keep them out of the mud.

Courtiers
These officials served a king at court and during visits.

Tower
Rooms built in a tower were the easiest to defend.

Kitchen
This was often built in the courtyard because of the risk of fire.

Lady Elaine then got busy arranging the place where the king would live. The east tower was always kept free for important visitors. With its three floors of comfortable rooms away from the rest of the castle, it would be safe and private.

However, it had never had a visitor as important as the king before. The rooms were clean and the furniture was good enough, but the walls and floors seemed rather bare. Lady Elaine decided that something would have to be done. She called the steward.

"Michael, we need coloured cloths to hang on the walls and more eastern carpets for the floors. Somebody will have to go to London, quickly. Not you – I need you here."

A kitchen fireplace

Next came the important job of deciding what to feed the king and his dozens of courtiers and the other officials who would be travelling with him. Lady Elaine had several meetings with the head cook.

The cook began by ordering supplies. Salted beef and bacon, pickled vegetables, and strings of onions soon filled the pantry. Later, fresh vegetables would arrive. The hunting parties would bring back fresh meat every day, and animals could be bought from the nearby farms.

He could count on a supply of fish, both from the castle moat and from the rivers and streams nearby. Also, near the castle stood a dovecote, the home to thousands of pigeons. These were normally kept for the winter, when meat might be scarce, but some could be added to the menu. The cook hoped the winter to come would not be too hard, because normally after the king stayed at a castle, there was a shortage of food for months to come.

Sacks of flour stood ready to be baked into bread and cakes. For such a large party, the oven would never stop working. Jars of honey to sweeten drinks and food were piled high. Fruit and herbs could be picked from the castle gardens. The cook also sent a message to a friend in a nearby castle, asking for some extra herbs and spices to add to his own.

Down in the cellar, the butler checked the wine barrels to make sure the wine was fit to drink. He also made the preparations to brew a large supply of beer so that it would be ready in time for the visit.

Pots and pans
Cooking was done over fires. This large pot was hung by chains over the heat.

Cook's knife
Sharp knives were needed to cut up animals killed by hunting parties.

Fish
This was either eaten fresh, or salted to keep it from rotting.

Hunting dogs
Packs of dogs were trained to follow animals by their smell. When cornered, boars would try to kill the dogs with their sharp tusks.

Deer hunting
Hunting deer helped to train young knights for war. They rode fast hunting horses called coursers.

Finally, one sunny morning, the king and his party rode up to the castle gates. It had been some time since Lord Thomas had seen him. They had got to know each other quite well during the wars in France, but since returning, Lord Thomas hadn't visited London very often. The king made the point when they met at the castle gate. "Since you are so unwilling to come and see me, Lord Thomas," he said, "I decided to come here."

Lord Thomas replied that it was merely London he disliked. "I think I can show you, my lord, that this estate can be interesting as well."

At the first opportunity, he did. He took the king to the forest with a party of knights and lords. They rode Thomas' best hunting horses.

A royal hunter and his pack of dogs chasing a deer.

The dogs soon found the smell of a deer and were off after it. Within a mile they had sight of it, and they chased it through the forest. The trees were not so thick, but it was still hard and dangerous to keep up with them. Finally, the dogs cornered it against a small cliff. The deer had nowhere to go, so it turned. It was a stag, a full-grown male, with a fine set of horns. It managed to throw back the first couple of dogs that moved in, but there were too many of them, and they pulled it down and killed it.

The king was pleased, and Lord Thomas was pleased that the dogs had killed a stag that was getting old.

Then the hunting party came across the trail of a wild pig, called a boar. After fighting with the entire dog pack, the boar ran into some young trees growing close together, where the dogs couldn't get at it. Finally, two knights on foot killed it with boar-spears.

Later that day, the king and Lord Thomas went hawking. They used Thomas' trained hawks to catch rabbits and small birds. Servants took the animals back to the castle for the feast. Lord Thomas was proud to serve his guests with food that came from his own land.

Hawking
Hawks trained for hunting were kept in a building called a mews or in a lord's rooms.

Wild boar
Served with apples, boar was a regular after-hunt dish.

The lords, ladies, knights, and courtiers began the feast by raising their metal cups. "To the king!" they shouted, and drank deeply.

Then servants carried in large metal dishes. These were piled high with roast meat. There was deer meat, known as venison, from the hunt, together with boar and various birds. There was also beef and pork and lamb.

Pheasants
Feathers were pushed back into cooked pheasants to make them look life-like.

At the table
People had their own knives and spoons but often shared bowls or cups.

The meat was eaten with vegetables, both fresh and pickled. Next, the servants brought in huge bowls which were full of fruit and nuts. There was even a ship made out of sugar. The musicians up in the gallery played music during the feast. They sang songs, and they blew trumpets when the servants brought in a special dish. They all feasted happily late into the night.

Bread plates
Servants ate off stale bread, which soaked up gravy. After the meat, they ate the bread.

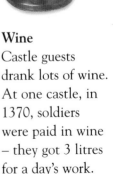

Wine
Castle guests drank lots of wine. At one castle, in 1370, soldiers were paid in wine – they got 3 litres for a day's work.

Early castles
The first castles were built in the 900s. They were made of earth and wood.

Bodiam Castle
This English castle is about 600 years old. The rich owner had seven halls built within its walls.

Old Stones

The great hall is silent now. There is no music any more, no singing, and no laughter. The castle kitchens are empty, the fires have long since gone out and the great ovens are cold. No one is hunting wild boar in the forest – there are no wild boar left, and the hunters are long since dead. There are no more knights, and no ladies. The castle that knew them all is in ruins.

At the end of the 1400s, bombards and cannons were becoming more common. They were able to destroy stone walls, and no castle could stand against them. Many lords moved into smaller, more comfortable homes.

Some families continued to live in their castles, either because they didn't have enough money to build a new home, or because they lived in an area that was not safe. Castles that could not stand against cannons were still able to give protection against local trouble. Other families would change the castle to make it more suitable to modern living.

But many castles were simply abandoned. If they stood in a remote area, they might remain almost untouched, apart from the damage done by the weather. However, if there were people living nearby, they usually just helped themselves to the stones and the wood. Within a few years there could be very little left.

Castle ghost
Years ago, a butler hanged himself in one of the towers of this Irish castle. His ghostly figure is said to walk the castle to this day.

Beeston Castle
This English castle was built on a rocky hill over 700 years ago.

Beeston today
The castle is now in ruins but the inner ditch remains. It cuts through solid rock!

Many of these castles are now open to visitors. If the castle is a complete ruin, it may still be possible to work out the position of the bakery, the kitchen, the brewhouse, the guardroom, and so on. In many castles, this work has been done for you, and the information is displayed on the walls. All it needs is the power of your imagination to take you back through the centuries.

In castles that are still standing, this may be much easier, but you might still have to imagine an old fireplace from the outline on the wall, or an outer building from the roofless ruin that remains. What might be more difficult is to get an idea of the noise and the smell of a place where so many people once lived together. Some castles provide audio-visual displays to help make the bridge between what used to be and what is there now.

A different approach is needed where the castle has continued to be a family home through the centuries. Rooms that once had walls of rough stone have long since been plastered, and painted or wallpapered in every style right up to the present day. Here, where a rough table once stood, there might be a television set, perhaps connected to a satellite receiver which stands in the place of a soldier on the roof.

However, it is still possible, if you give yourself time to think, to imagine part of how it was then.

Experts dig up the ground around castles looking for things from the past. Often the best place to find clues is in the rubbish pit which can be found near every castle. Animal bones, the remains of vegetables, and seeds can give clues to what people ate. Old coins can be dated to the time of a particular king or queen. If the searchers are lucky, they might find something bigger, like a sword, helmet, or shield.

Decorative old coins
These show important people and events from the past.

Graves can also tell us a lot. Important people might be buried near, or even inside, the castle, and if there was an attack, the bodies of the soldiers who died will not be far away. We can tell the age of people when they died, and often what disease or injury killed them. Occupations also leave their mark. A bowman, for instance, will have bones of a different thickness on each arm, and usually signs of back strain. Also today, using computers, we can take a skull and build up a reasonably accurate picture of how the person looked.

Staircases
These almost always turned to the right so that a right-handed attacker, climbing up, had no space to swing his sword.

The surprising thing is that they looked much the same as people today. They were smaller on average, but their faces were the same as the faces you might see in any local street. They lived in the past, and we would find their way of life very strange, but they were people just like us. Why not visit a castle and meet them?

Glossary

artisans
Skilled workers such as carpenters, metalworkers, and stonemasons.

battlements
The tops of castle walls from where soldiers can shoot at attackers.

bombard
A cannon that fires large stone cannonballs.

catapult
A machine for throwing large rocks.

coat of arms
The design an upper-class family put on their shields and clothes.

courtiers
Upper-class people who worked closely with the king.

courtyard
The open ground inside the castle walls.

drawbridge
A bridge that can be pulled up and let down.

dubbing
When a king or queen touches a squire on the shoulders with a sword to make him a knight.

estate
All of a lord's lands and properties.

garrison
The soldiers who defend a castle.

gatehouse
A large tower that surrounds the main gate.

gauntlets
Metal gloves that are worn as part of a suit of armour.

hostages
Prisoners who are sent back to their friends and families in return for payment.

joust
A competition between two knights in which each tries to knock the other off his horse.

lance
A very long weapon with a pointed end.

looters
Attackers who take away things of value.

lord
An upper-class man, usually also a knight, who owns a lot of land and property.

mace
A stick with a metal end that can break bones.

master mason
A skilled man who designs castles.

minstrels
Travelling musicians who sing and play to entertain.

moat
A ditch filled with water around a castle.

mummers
A group of travelling actors who put on plays.

page
A boy who will later be trained as a knight.

peasants
People who work on a lord's land in return for growing things to feed themselves.

pedlar
Someone who travels and sells small things.

scaffolding
A temporary wooden framework erected around a building.

sentry
A soldier who watches to see if enemies are approaching.

siege camp
A camp where soldiers live while they are trying to capture a castle.

siege tower
A large, covered tower that can be pushed up to the castle walls.

squire
A teenage boy who is training to be a knight.

writ
A document that gives permission or changes the law.